Dinosaur Boog

MW00612913

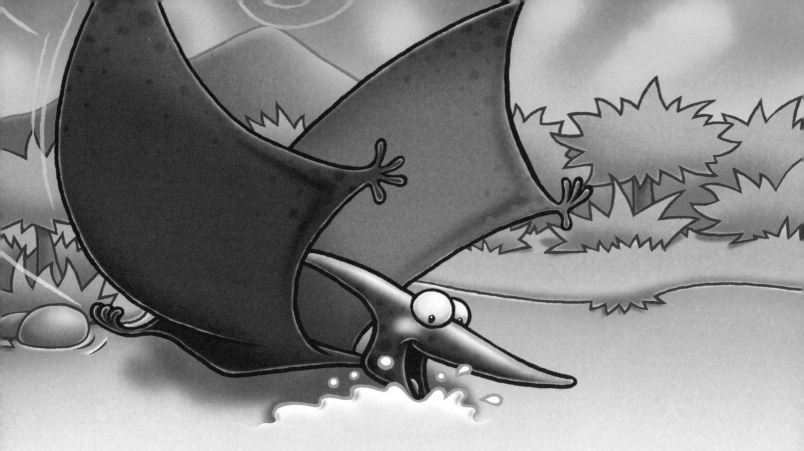

Pterosaur had wings and could fly.
She'd swoop in the swamp, then up in the sky.

The ancestor of birds, they say.
I wish she were here today.

Tyrannosaurus Rex, king of the swamp.
He'd growl and snarl, and then he'd go CHOMP.

He ate meat. He was a carnivore.
They'd all hide when Rex would roar.

5

Do the dinosaur boogie; bounce around.
Hands like claws, make a growling sound—"grrrr!"

Stomp, stomp, stomp the ground.
Then wiggle and turn around.

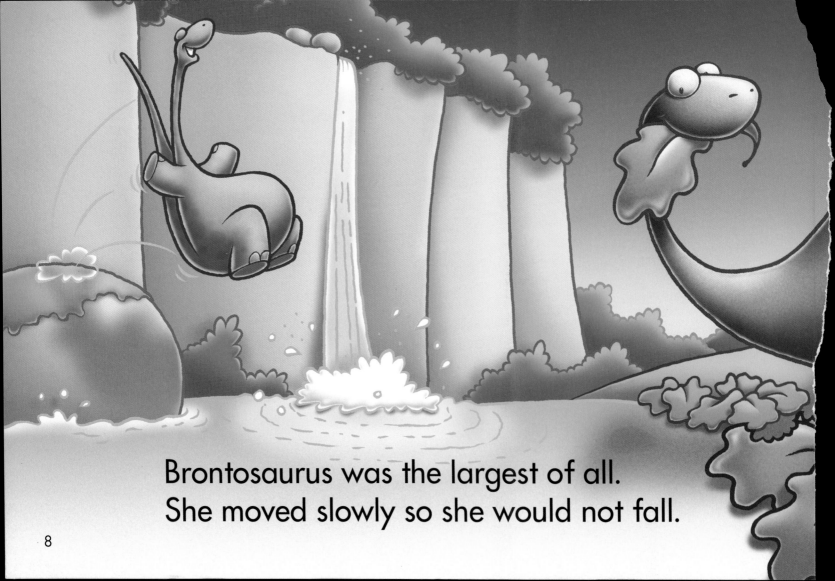

Brontosaurus was the largest of all.
She moved slowly so she would not fall.

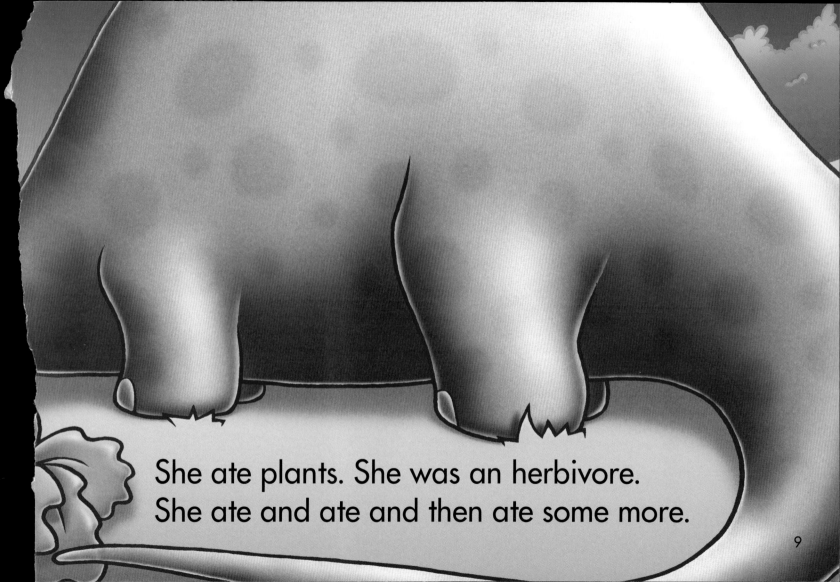

She ate plants. She was an herbivore.
She ate and ate and then ate some more.

9

Triceratops had three horns on his head.
I'd like to see one, but now they're all dead.

Where, oh, where did the dinosaurs go?
I guess we'll never know!

Do the dinosaur boogie; bounce around.
Hands like claws, make a growling sound—"grrrr!"
Stomp, stomp, stomp the ground.
Then wiggle and turn around.